This
Book
Belongs
To _Katie Alderson_

2

Grolier Enterprises Inc.
SHERMAN TURNPIKE, DANBURY, CONNECTICUT 06816

Book Club Edition

The STORY Of ISAAC And REBECKAH

An ALICE IN BIBLELAND Storybook ®

Written by Alice Joyce Davidson
Designed by Victoria Marshall

A little girl named Alice
Kept busy all day through.
She went to school, she played with friends
And helped with housework, too.

Whenever she had extra time
She'd curl up in her nook
And read a favorite story
From her Bible storybook.

One day she read of Isaac,
When suddenly she heard
A tapping on her window
From the friendly airmail bird.

Alice opened up her window.
The bird perched on her head.
He dropped a letter on her lap
And this is what it said:

"Reading is the magic key
To take you where you want to be."

The book that Alice held became
A great big picture screen.
Alice walked through it to Bibleland
And came upon this scene.

She saw a man named Isaac
Who looked sad as he could be.
He mourned his mother who had died
And missed her terribly.

Abraham, his father, said,
"What Isaac needs right now,
Is a wife with kind and gentle ways
To comfort him somehow.

"But among these godless Canaanites,
There's no one he should wed.
His wife should come from Haran,
Where my people live instead."

So he told his trusted servant,
"I've a task for you to do.
Promise me you'll do exactly
What I want you to.

"Go to the land where I was born,
And it is there you'll find
A maiden from my people
Who's loving, sweet and kind.

"Tell her my son, Isaac,
Is looking for a wife.
Then bring her here to Canaan
To begin her married life."

The servant took ten camels
Loaded down with gifts that day
And started off to Haran
Which was very far away.

When he arrived in Haran,
He prayed to God above
To help him find a maiden
Who'd bring Isaac joy and love.

He prayed, "Dear God, please let it be
The kind of maiden who,
After offering me a drink
Will care for my camels, too."

A maiden named Rebeckah
Came by in just a while.
She was beautiful and graceful
And she had a friendly smile.

She drew some water from the well.
The servant saw her there.
He asked her if she had a bit
Of water she could spare.

Rebeckah offered him a drink,
And then when he was done,
She saw his thirsty camels
Who had traveled in the sun.

Rebeckah got some water
For the thirsty camels, too.
The servant was quite happy
For his prayer was coming true.

He knew Rebeckah was the one
Picked by God above
To be the wife of Isaac
And to fill his heart with love.

He gave Rebeckah jewelry,
Then asked her right away
If he could meet her family
And stay with them that day.

She said her father, Bethu'el,
Had room and food to spare,
And the servant and his camels
Would be very welcome there.

The servant said a thankful prayer.
He was so elated
For he knew that Abraham
And Bethu'el were related.

The servant told her family
How he was sent to find
Someone to marry Isaac,
A maiden sweet and kind.

He said, "I've found the perfect one
To wed my master's son.
If you'll let Rebeckah go with me,
God's wish will then be done."

Rebeckah's folks gave their consent,
And without too much delay
Rebeckah and her servants
And her nurse went on their way.

Isaac met Rebeckah,
And loved her from the start.
Abraham was happy
For the joy in Isaac's heart.

The time had come for Alice
To leave that Bible scene.
She came back home by walking through
The giant picture screen.

Then Alice thought, "I've learned a lot
Today in Bibleland,
For Abraham and Isaac
Were part of what God planned.

"God had promised Abraham,
A long, long time ago,
That he would start a nation
That would prosper and would grow...

"And since Isaac was his only son,
Isaac had to have a wife
Who would share in his belief in God
And lead a faith-filled life.

"And though God is very busy
With a million things to do,
He helped the servant find Rebeckah,
So His promise could come true!"